The Big Book of Flute Songs

HLE

Hal Leonard Europe
Distributed by Music Sales

Exclusive Distributors:
Music Sales Limited
8/9 Frith Street, London W1D 3JB, England.

Order No. HLE90001045
ISBN 0-7119-8276-7
This book © Copyright 2005 by Hal Leonard Europe

Cover design by Chloë Alexander
Cover photograph by George Taylor
Printed in the USA

Your Guarantee of Quality
As publishers, we strive to produce every book to the highest commercial standards.

The book has been carefully designed to minimise awkward page turns and to make playing from it a real pleasure.

Throughout, the printing and binding have been planned to ensure a sturdy, attractive publication which should give years of enjoyment.

If your copy fails to meet our high standards, please inform us and we will gladly replace it.

www.musicsales.com

ACHY BREAKY HEART
(Don't Tell My Heart)

Words and Music by
DON VON TRESS

FLUTE

Steady beat

To Coda ⊕

D.S. al Coda

⊕ **CODA**

ALL MY LOVING

Flute

Words and Music by
JOHN LENNON and PAUL McCARTNEY

ALL FOR LOVE

From Walt Disney Pictures' THE THREE MUSKETEERS

Flute

Words and Music by BRYAN ADAMS,
ROBERT JOHN "MUTT" LANGE and MICHAEL KAMEN

D.S. al Coda   Coda

ALL SHOOK UP

FLUTE

Words and Music by OTIS BLACKWELL
and ELVIS PRESLEY

Medium Shuffle Rhythm

AND I LOVE HER

FLUTE

Words and Music by
JOHN LENNON and PAUL McCARTNEY

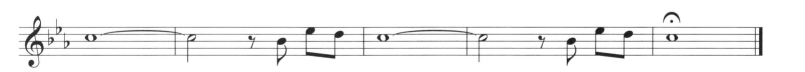

BE OUR GUEST

from Walt Disney's BEAUTY AND THE BEAST

Lyrics by HOWARD ASHMAN
Music by ALAN MENKEN

FLUTE

Small notes are optional

BEAUTY AND THE BEAST

From Walt Disney's BEAUTY AND THE BEAST

FLUTE

Lyrics by HOWARD ASHMAN
Music by ALAN MENKEN

BÉSAME MUCHO
(Kiss Me Much)

Music and Spanish Words by CONSUELO VELAZQUEZ
English Words by SUNNY SKYLAR

FLUTE

BLACKBIRD

Flute

Words and Music by JOHN LENNON
and PAUL McCARTNEY

Slowly

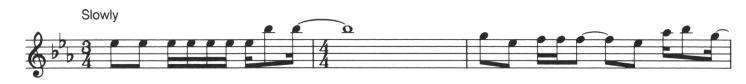

BLUE SUEDE SHOES

Words and Music by
CARL LEE PERKINS

FLUTE

Bright tempo (not too fast)

BOOGIE WOOGIE BUGLE BOY

from BUCK PRIVATES

FLUTE

Words and Music by
DON RAYE and HUGHIE PRINCE

BORN TO BE WILD

Words and Music by
MARS BONFIRE

Flute

BRAZIL

Words and Music by
S.K. RUSSELL and ARY BARROSO

FLUTE

BRIDGE OVER TROUBLED WATER

FLUTE

Words and Music by
PAUL SIMON

Medium slow Ballad

BRING HIM HOME

Flute

Music by CLAUDE-MICHEL SCHÖNBERG
Lyrics by HERBERT KRETZMER and ALAIN BOUBLIL

BYE BYE LOVE

Words and Music by FELICE BRYANT
and BOUDLEAUX BRYANT

Flute

CALIFORNIA DREAMIN'

Words and Music by JOHN PHILLIPS
and MICHELLE PHILLIPS

Flute

Medium Rock Beat

CAN YOU FEEL THE LOVE TONIGHT

From Walt Disney Pictures' THE LION KING

Flute

Music by ELTON JOHN
Lyrics by TIM RICE

Pop Ballad

Small notes optional

CHANTILLY LACE

FLUTE

Words and Music by
J.P. RICHARDSON

Moderate Boogie Woogie

Spoken: Oh, Ba - by, that's - a

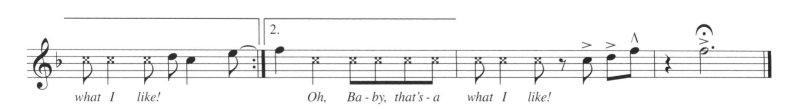

what I like!   Oh, Ba - by, that's - a   what I like!

CANDLE IN THE WIND

Music by ELTON JOHN
Words by BERNIE TAUPIN

FLUTE

CHAPEL OF LOVE

Words and Music by PHIL SPECTOR,
ELLIE GREENWICH and JEFF BARRY

Flute

CLIMB EV'RY MOUNTAIN

Flute

Lyrics by OSCAR HAMMERSTEIN II
Music by RICHARD RODGERS

CIRCLE OF LIFE

from Walt Disney Pictures' THE LION KING

Music by ELTON JOHN
Lyrics by TIM RICE

FLUTE

COLORS OF THE WIND

From Walt Disney's POCAHONTAS

Flute

Music by ALAN MENKEN
Lyrics by STEPHEN SCHWARTZ

COME TOGETHER

Flute

Words and Music by JOHN LENNON
and PAUL McCARTNEY

Slowly

A DAY IN THE LIFE

FLUTE

Words and Music by JOHN LENNON
and PAUL McCARTNEY

DEDICATED TO THE ONE I LOVE

Words and Music by LOWMAN PAULING
and RALPH BASS

FLUTE

DON'T BE CRUEL
(To A Heart That's True)

flute

Words and Music by
OTIS BLACKWELL and ELVIS PRESLEY

DON'T CRY FOR ME ARGENTINA

from EVITA

Words by TIM RICE
Music by ANDREW LLOYD WEBBER

Flute

DREAM BABY
(How Long Must I Dream)

Words and Music by
CINDY WALKER

FLUTE

Moderately

DREAM LOVER

Words and Music by
BOBBY DARIN

FLUTE

Moderately

THEME FROM E.T. (THE EXTRA-TERRESTRIAL)

from the Universal Picture E.T. (THE EXTRA–TERRESTRIAL)

FLUTE

Music by
JOHN WILLIAMS

EDELWEISS

Flute

Lyrics by OSCAR HAMMERSTEIN II
Music by RICHARD RODGERS

With gentle motion

rit.

EIGHT DAYS A WEEK

FLUTE

Words and Music by JOHN LENNON
and PAUL McCARTNEY

EL CUMBANCHERO

Words and Music by
RAFAEL HERNANDEZ

FLUTE

ELEANOR RIGBY

FLUTE

Words and Music by JOHN LENNON
and PAUL McCARTNEY

FEVER

Flute

Words and Music by
JOHN DAVENPORT and EDDIE COOLEY

FIELDS OF GOLD

FLUTE

Music and Lyrics by
STING

THE FOOL ON THE HILL

FLUTE

Words and Music by JOHN LENNON
and PAUL McCARTNEY

THE GIRL FROM IPANEMA
(Garôta De Ipanema)

English Words by NORMAN GIMBEL
Original Words by VINICIUS de MORAES
Music by ANTONIO CARLOS JOBIM

FLUTE

GO THE DISTANCE
From Walt Disney Pictures' HERCULES

Flute

Music by ALAN MENKEN
Lyrics by DAVID ZIPPEL

GOD BLESS' THE CHILD

FLUTE

Words and Music by
ARTHUR HERZOG Jr. and BILLIE HOLIDAY

Slowly with feeling

HAVE I TOLD YOU LATELY

Flute

Words and Music by
VAN MORRISON

GOD HELP THE OUTCASTS

FLUTE

Music by ALAN MENKEN
Lyrics by STEPHEN SCHWARTZ

GRANADA

By ERNESTO LECUONA

FLUTE

HELLO, GOODBYE

FLUTE

Words and Music by JOHN LENNON
and PAUL McCARTNEY

HERE, THERE AND EVERYWHERE

FLUTE

Words and Music by JOHN LENNON
and PAUL McCARTNEY

HEY JUDE

FLUTE

Words and Music by
JOHN LENNON and PAUL McCARTNEY

I DON'T KNOW HOW TO LOVE HIM

from JESUS CHRIST SUPERSTAR

Words by TIM RICE
Music by ANDREW LLOYD WEBBER

flute

I DREAMED A DREAM

Flute

Music by CLAUDE-MICHEL SCHÖNBERG
Lyrics by HERBERT KRETZMER
Original Text by ALAIN BOUBLIL and JEAN-MARC NATEL

I GET ALONG WITHOUT YOU VERY WELL
(Except Sometimes)

Flute

Words and Music by HOAGY CARMICHAEL
Inspired by a poem written by J.B. THOMPSON

Slowly, with expression

To Coda

D.C. al Coda

CODA

I GOT YOU
(I Feel Good)

Words and Music by
JAMES BROWN

FLUTE

I LEFT MY HEART IN SAN FRANCISCO

FLUTE

Words by DOUGLASS CROSS
Music by GEORGE CORY

Slowly

I REMEMBER YOU

(From The Paramount Picture "THE FLEET'S IN")

Flute

Words by JOHNNY MERCER
Music by VICTOR SCHERTZINGER

Moderately, not too fast, expressively

I SAY A LITTLE PRAYER

Featured in the TriStar Motion Picture MY BEST FRIEND'S WEDDING

FLUTE

Lyric by HAL DAVID
Music by BURT BACHARACH

I WANT YOU, I NEED YOU, I LOVE YOU

Words by MAURICE MYSELS
Music by IRA KOSLOFF

FLUTE

I WILL

Flute

Words and Music by JOHN LENNON
and PAUL McCARTNEY

Moderately

I'D DO ANYTHING FOR LOVE
(But I Won't Do That)

FLUTE

Words and Music by
JIM STEINMAN

IF I EVER LOSE MY FAITH IN YOU

FLUTE

Music and Lyrics by
STING

IF I FELL

Flute

Words and Music by JOHN LENNON
and PAUL McCARTNEY

Moderato

IMAGINE

Words and Music by
JOHN LENNON

Flute

IN MY LIFE

FLUTE

Words and Music by JOHN LENNON
and PAUL McCARTNEY

ISN'T IT ROMANTIC?
(From The Paramount Picture "LOVE ME TONIGHT")

Words by LORENZ HART
Music by RICHARD RODGERS

Flute

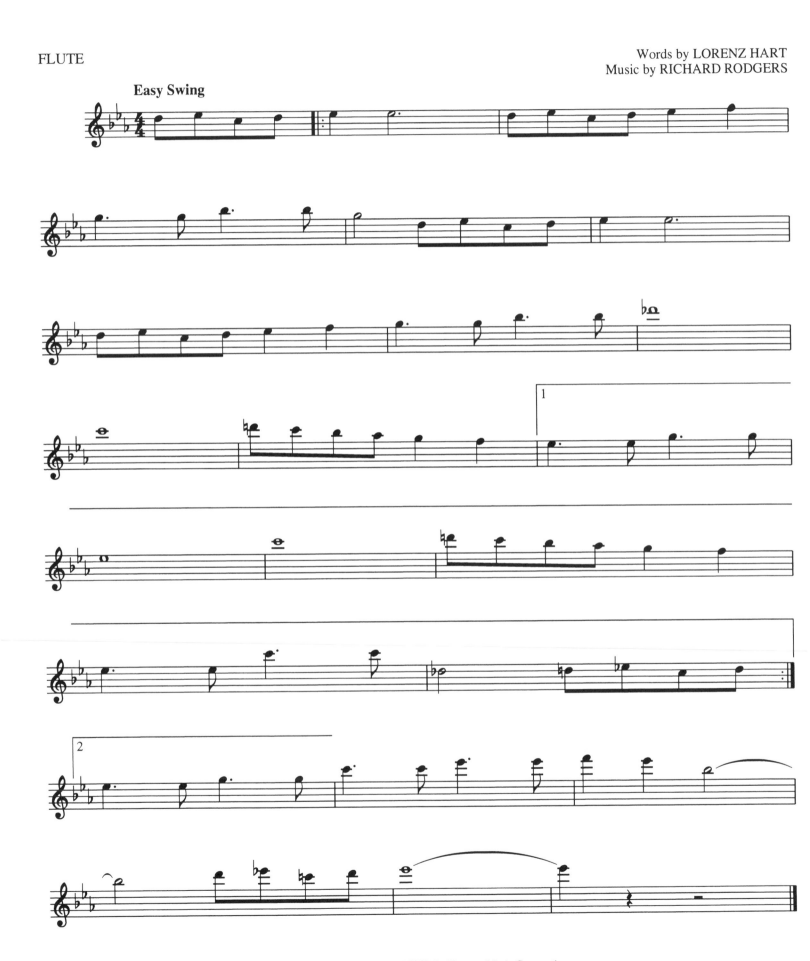

ITSY BITSY TEENIE WEENIE
YELLOW POLKADOT BIKINI

Words and Music by PAUL VANCE
and LEE POCKRISS

FLUTE

Brightly, with humor

JAILHOUSE ROCK

Words and Music by
JERRY LEIBER and MIKE STOLLER

FLUTE

Moderately

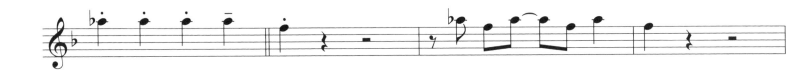

LET IT BE

FLUTE

Words and Music by
JOHN LENNON and PAUL McCARTNEY

THE LONG AND WINDING ROAD

Flute

Words and Music by
JOHN LENNON and PAUL McCARTNEY

LOUIE, LOUIE

FLUTE

Words and Music by
RICHARD BERRY

LOVE IS ALL AROUND

featured on the Motion Picture Soundtrack FOUR WEDDINGS AND A FUNERAL

Words and Music by
REG PRESLEY

Flute

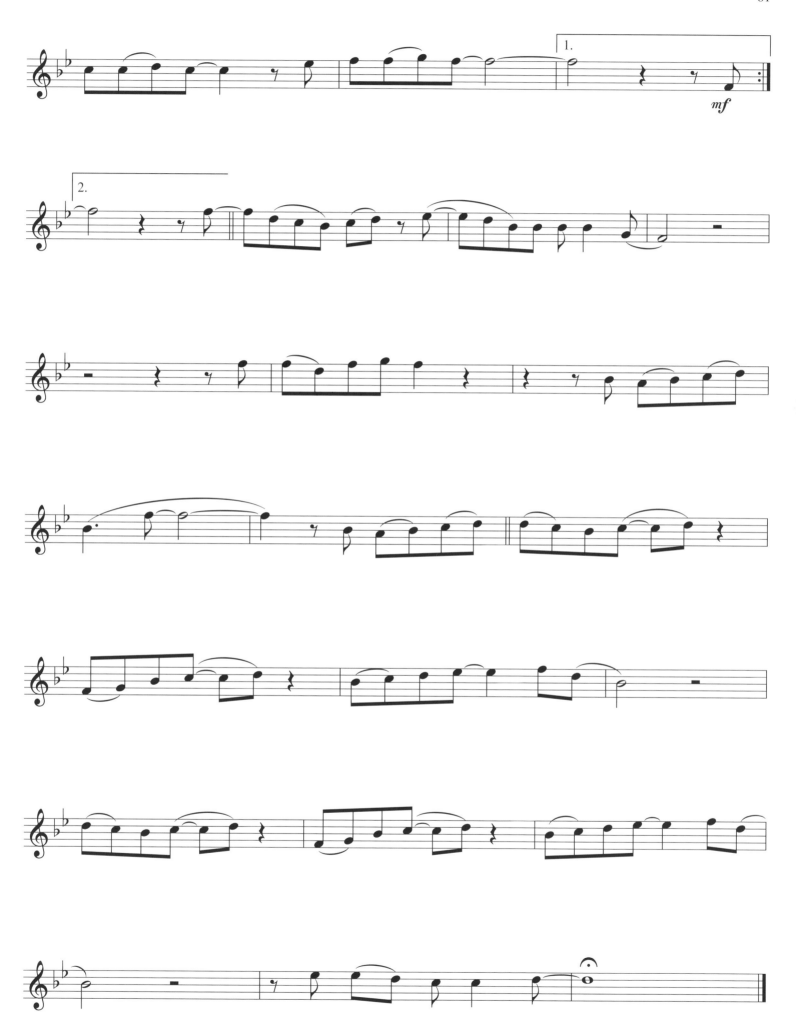

LOVE ME TENDER

Flute

Words and Music by
ELVIS PRESLEY and VERA MATSON

Moderately slow

LOVE STORY
Theme from the Paramount Picture LOVE STORY

FLUTE

Music by FRANCIS LAI

MALAGUEÑA
from the Spanish Suite ANDALUCIA

Music and Spanish Lyric by ERNESTO LECUONA
English Lyric by MARIAN BANKS

FLUTE

MAMBO No. 5
(A Little Bit Of...)

FLUTE

Original Music by DAMASO PEREZ PRADO
Words by LOU BEGA and ZIPPY

MAS QUE NADA

Words and Music by
JORGE BEN

FLUTE

MEDITATION

(Meditacâo)

Music by ANTONIO CARLOS JOBIM
Original Words by NEWTON MENDONÇA
English Words by NORMAN GIMBEL

FLUTE

Relaxed

MICHELLE

Flute

Words and Music by JOHN LENNON
and PAUL McCARTNEY

Moderately

MISSION: IMPOSSIBLE THEME

From the Paramount Television Series MISSION: IMPOSSIBLE

FLUTE

By LALO SCHIFRIN

MOON RIVER

From the Paramount Picture BREAKFAST AT TIFFANY'S

FLUTE

Words by JOHNNY MERCER
Music by HENRY MANCINI

MOONLIGHT BECOMES YOU

(From The Paramount Picture "ROAD TO MOROCCO")

FLUTE

Words by JOHNNY BURKE
Music by JAMES VAN HEUSEN

Slowly with expression

MY FAVORITE THINGS

FLUTE

Lyrics by OSCAR HAMMERSTEIN II
Music by RICHARD RODGERS

MY OLD FLAME

(From The Paramount Picture "BELLE OF THE NINETIES")

FLUTE

Words and Music by ARTHUR JOHNSTON
and SAM COSLOW

Moderately

THE NEARNESS OF YOU

From the Paramount Picture ROMANCE IN THE DARK

FLUTE

Words by NED WASHINGTON
Music by HOAGY CARMICHAEL

A NIGHT IN TUNISIA

Music by JOHN "DIZZY" GILLESPIE
and FRANK PAPARELLI

Flute

Medium fast

ONE NOTE SAMBA
(Samba De Uma Nota So)

FLUTE

Original Lyrics by NEWTON MENDONCA
English Lyrics by ANTONIO CARLOS JOBIM
Music by ANTONIO CARLOS JOBIM

PEGGY SUE

Flute

Words and Music by JERRY ALLISON,
NORMAN PETTY and BUDDY HOLLY

PENNY LANE

FLUTE

Words and Music by JOHN LENNON
and PAUL McCARTNEY

PERFIDIA

Words and Music by
ALBERTO DOMINGUEZ

FLUTE

QUIET NIGHTS OF QUIET STARS
(Corcovado)

English Words by GENE LEES
Original Words and Music by ANTONIO CARLOS JOBIM

FLUTE

RAIDERS MARCH

From the Paramount Motion Picture RAIDERS OF THE LOST ARK

FLUTE

JOHN WILLIAMS

REFLECTION
From Walt Disney Pictures' MULAN

Music by MATTHEW WILDER
Lyrics by DAVID ZIPPEL

Flute

ROCKIN' ROBIN

Words and Music by
J. THOMAS

FLUTE

Bright Rock tempo
To Coda
1
2
D.S. al Coda
CODA

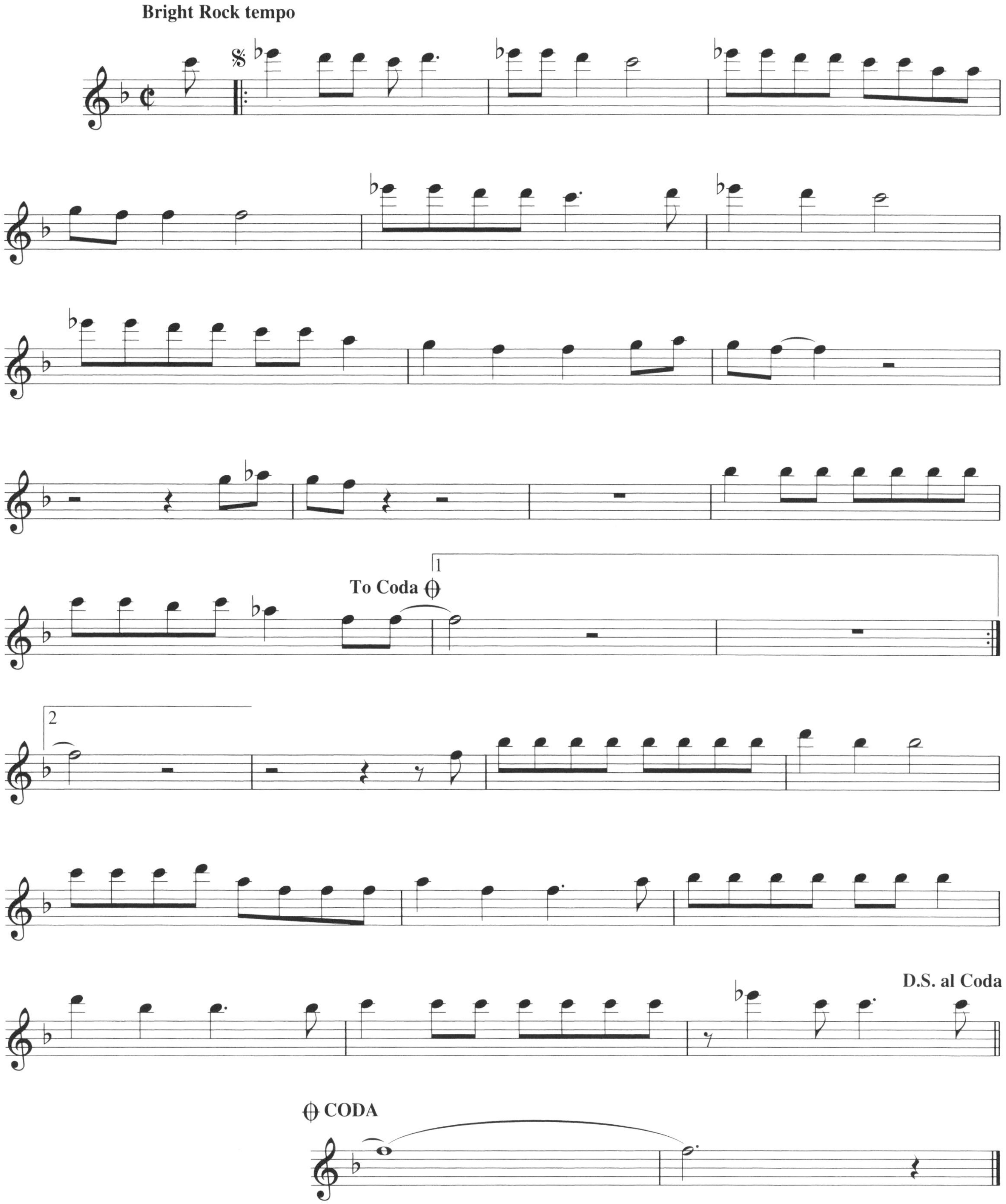

RUBY BABY

Words and Music by JERRY LEIBER
and MIKE STOLLER

FLUTE

SATIN DOLL

FLUTE

By DUKE ELLINGTON

SAVE THE LAST DANCE FOR ME

Words and Music by DOC POMUS
and MORT SHUMAN

FLUTE

Moderately, with a beat

THEME FROM "SCHINDLER'S LIST"

from the Universal Motion Picture SCHINDLER'S LIST

FLUTE

Composed by JOHN WILLIAMS

SEARCHIN'

Words and Music by JERRY LEIBER
and MIKE STOLLER

FLUTE

Not too fast, with a strong afterbeat

SO NICE
(Summer Samba)

FLUTE

Original Words and Music by
MARCOS VALLE and PAULO SERGIO VALLE
English Words by NORMAN GIMBEL

Relaxed Bossa Nova

SOMEDAY
From Walt Disney's THE HUNCHBACK OF NOTRE DAME

FLUTE

Music by ALAN MENKEN
Lyrics by STEPHEN SCHWARTZ

SOMETHING

FLUTE

Words and Music by
GEORGE HARRISON

SOMETIMES

FLUTE

Words and Music by
JORGEN ELOFSSON

Moderately, not too fast

Small note optional

rit.

SPLISH SPLASH

Flute

Words and Music by
BOBBY DARIN and MURRAY KAUFMAN

STELLA BY STARLIGHT

From the Paramount Picture THE UNINVITED

FLUTE

Words by NED WASHINGTON
Music by VICTOR YOUNG

STRAWBERRY FIELDS FOREVER

FLUTE

Words and Music by JOHN LENNON
and PAUL McCARTNEY

STOP

FLUTE

Words and Music by ANDY WATKINS,
PAUL WILSON and SPICE GIRLS

STRUTTIN' WITH SOME BARBECUE

FLUTE

Words and Music by
LILLIAN HARDIN ARMSTRONG and DON RAYE

SUMMERTIME BLUES

Words and Music by EDDIE COCHRAN
and JERRY CAPEHART

FLUTE

SUNSHINE OF YOUR LOVE

Words and Music by JACK BRUCE,
PETE BROWN and ERIC CLAPTON

FLUTE

TAKE THE "A" TRAIN

FLUTE

Words and Music by
BILLY STRAYHORN

TAKIN' CARE OF BUSINESS

Words and Music by
RANDY BACHMAN

FLUTE

Driving Rock

TANGERINE

From the Paramount Picture THE FLEET'S IN

Words by JOHNNY MERCER
Music by VICTOR SCHERTZINGER

FLUTE

THAT OLD BLACK MAGIC

From the Paramount Picture STAR SPANGLED RHYTHM

FLUTE

Words by JOHNNY MERCER
Music by HAROLD ARLEN

THAT'LL BE THE DAY

Words and Music by JERRY ALLISON,
NORMAN PETTY and BUDDY HOLLY

Flute

Moderately with a beat

UNDER THE BOARDWALK

Words and Music by ARTIE RESNICK
and KENNY YOUNG

FLUTE

Moderately, with a beat

UNINVITED

From the Motion Picture CITY OF ANGELS

FLUTE

Words and Music by
ALANIS MORISSETTE

UP WHERE WE BELONG

From the Paramount Picture AN OFFICER AND A GENTLEMAN

FLUTE

Words by WILL JENNINGS
Music by BUFFY SAINTE-MARIE and JACK NITZSCHE

WAKE UP LITTLE SUSIE

Words and Music by BOUDLEAUX BRYANT
and FELICE BRYANT

Flute

A WHOLE NEW WORLD
(Aladdin's Theme)
From Walt Disney's ALADDIN

Flute

Music by ALAN MENKEN
Lyrics by TIM RICE

WONDERFUL TONIGHT

Flute

Words and Music by
ERIC CLAPTON

WOODCHOPPER'S BALL

FLUTE

By JOE BISHOP
and WOODY HERMAN

WOOLY BULLY

FLUTE

Words and Music by
DOMINGO SAMUDIO

YELLOW SUBMARINE

FLUTE

Words and Music by JOHN LENNON
and PAUL McCARTNEY

YESTERDAY

Words and Music by
JOHN LENNON and PAUL McCARTNEY

FLUTE

Moderately, with expression

YOU MUST LOVE ME

From the Cinergi Motion Picture EVITA

Flute

Words by TIM RICE
Music by ANDREW LLOYD WEBBER

(YOU DRIVE ME) CRAZY

FLUTE

Words and Music by
JORGEN ELOFSSON, MARTIN SANDBERG,
PER MAGNUSSON and DAVID KREUGER

YOU'LL BE IN MY HEART
(Pop Version)
From Walt Disney Pictures' TARZAN®

FLUTE

Words and Music by
PHIL COLLINS

YOU'VE GOT A FRIEND IN ME

From Walt Disney's TOY STORY

FLUTE

Music and Lyrics by
RANDY NEWMAN

YOUNG BLOOD

Words and Music by JERRY LEIBER,
MIKE STOLLER and DOC POMUS

Flute

ZOOT SUIT RIOT

Flute

Words and Music by
STEVE PERRY